For Charlee

This book is also for Baby Chloe and Baby Landon
and all the other NICU babies and their families.

CHAPTER 1
THE PLAN

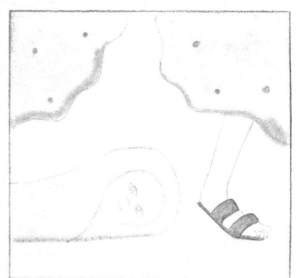

Oh, it's okay. They are just covering c-sections. I don't need to be there for that.

I'm so prepared, there's no way I'm not having a natural birth.

And that's all you need to know about c-sections.

Next, we are going to work on birth plans.

A birth plan lets your medical team know your preferences for labor and delivery.

Work with your partner on this preparedness guide.

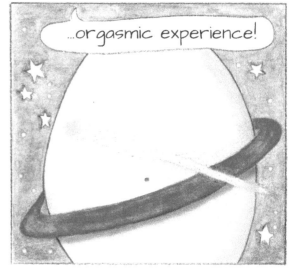

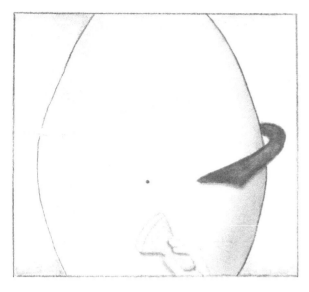

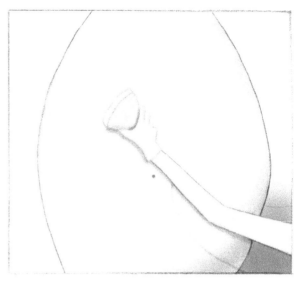

Here is your paperw...

Oh, you guys! It's a lot isn't it?

This doesn't change the fact that you both still get to care for and be parents to this child.

If the baby were to come today, would you be ready at home?

A plan is in place now. Go home, get ready and enjoy it!

CHAPTER 2
CHANGE OF PLANS

I'm so impressed you guys are going to cloth diaper.

But you are the kind of couple who can do it all.

Time for a game. Let's see how well you know your nursery rhymes.

First question: how old was the pease porridge in the pot?

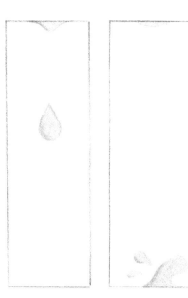

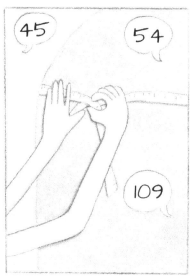

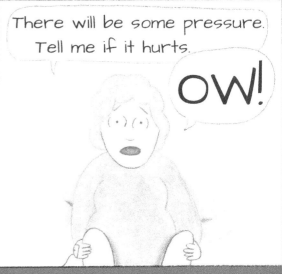

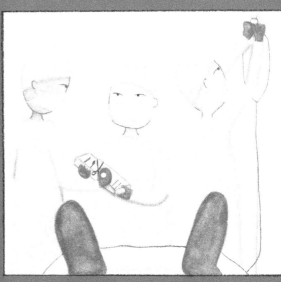

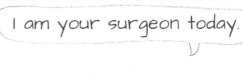

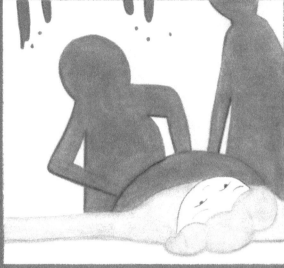

CHAPTER 3
QUEST

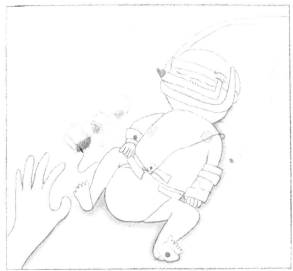

33

Look out! You don't want to get between this mama and her baby!

You are just in time for a diaper change.

I've got this!

You're not supposed to be up.

I'm fine.

35

It's okay. We'll call her "Baby Girl" for now.

What about the name we picked out?

It's not an ordinary name. What if it makes things even harder for her?

Do you want to hold her now, Dad?

Umm. Okay.

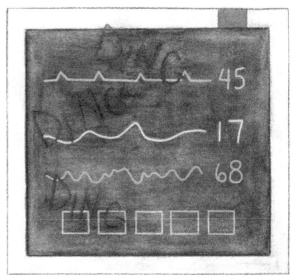

40

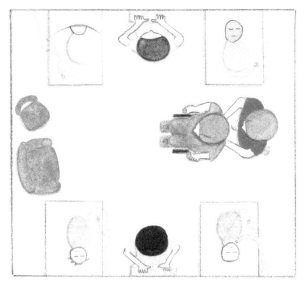

Finally! I'm glad we got here before you could walk away.

Let me show you how to do skin to skin.

Oh wow! This is the best thing ever!

mumble. mumble. mumble. The spell has broken. mumble. mumble.

What an exciting day!

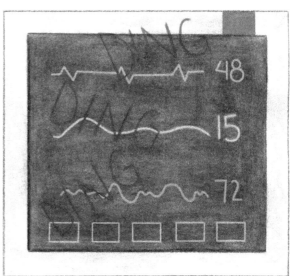

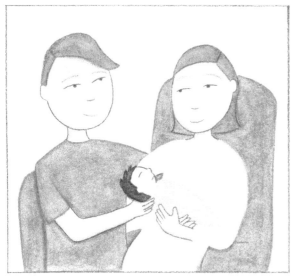

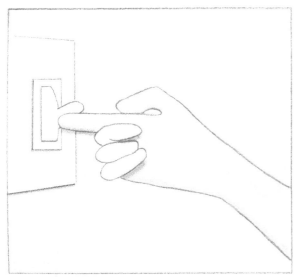

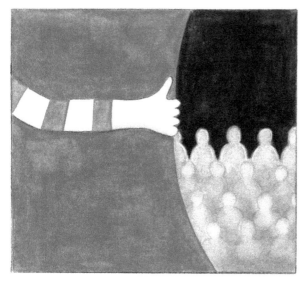

CHAPTER 4
OUTSIDER

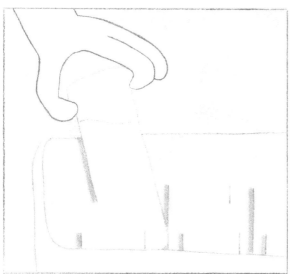

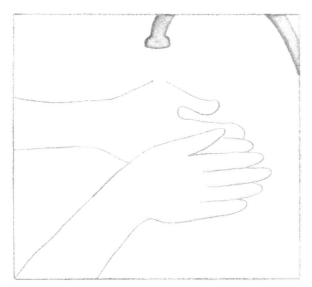

Good morning Charlee!

Since we can't be home, we'll make the best of our day here.

I brought books and as a former camp counselor...

I have enough songs to sing through next week.

There's nowhere I would rather be.

As long as I can be with you.

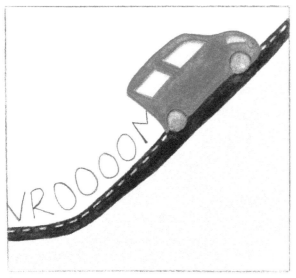

67

CHAPTER 5
TRICK OR TREAT

Happy Halloween Charlee!

Sweetest pumpkin in the patch.

OMG! You guys are so cute!

We need to talk with you about what happened.

Have a seat.

A swallow study has determined that Charlee can not eat by mouth.

So we'll continue using the tube through her nose?

She needs something long term.

What we suggest is called a G-tube.

Surgery is required for placement.

We can't release her until she can safely feed.

We knew you didn't have time to decorate.

And we wanted to come keep you company.

You can say no...

But would you want to go and see the decorations?

No, but you're right.

It'll be good for us.

They want to put a G-tube into her belly.

That sounds scary.

We don't want to do it.

This might be the thing that breaks the spell.

CHAPTER 6
FANTASY OR REALITY

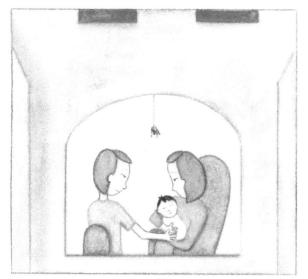

We are just about ready. Do you have any questions?

Just how safe is this surgery?

It's so common. I do it all the time.

It's my bread and butter.

Let's go get coffee.

I'm going to pump.

That's the third time this hour.

Everyone here is doing something to help Charlee. I'm not going to sit here and feel like there's nothing I can do for her.

She's out. You can see her.

Oh, Charlee...

She's doing really well. The attending physician should be here soon for daily rounds.

Come gather around.

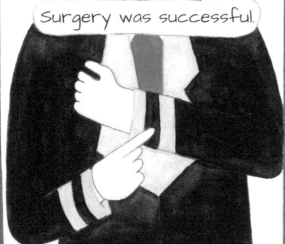

So for the next and greatest act we will be performing...

THE TRACHEOSTOMY!

Next patient is a nine week female. This one has a trach!

Hi! I'm from dietetics. Are you considering formula?

Maybe I should come back at a better time.

Can we get some help? There's a mom down.

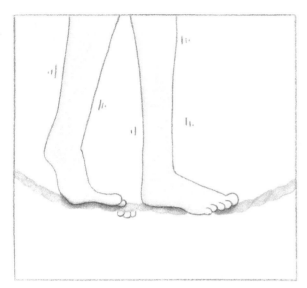

CHAPTER 7
NO WAY AROUND IT

Ugh! As if Charlee is some sort of side show experiment.

It was pretty bad but we have no information about a trach. For all we know that doctor was trying to look exciting to his students.

For today, just go up there and love her.

And if we have to...

We'll kidnap her when I come up there after work.

The mama bear and the baby bear set off to the berry patch together.

Is this a good time?

KNOCK
KNOCK

I guess.

So...they are recommending a tracheostomy.

Yeah. I heard.

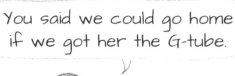

You said we could go home if we got her the G-tube.

Charlee has obstructions in her airway which are preventing oxygen from reaching her lungs. A trach would bypass the obstructions to easily deliver oxygen to her lungs.

You need to get here now.

Charlee stopped breathing. It was really scary.

They put this nasal trumpet thing in and she can breathe.

I have to get off the phone. Please come as soon as you possibly can.

92

I came as fast as I could. What's going on?

There was nothing I could do to help her.

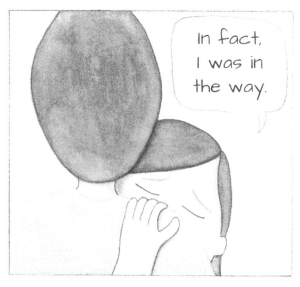

In fact, I was in the way.

I thought I was coming to say goodbye.

Ahem.

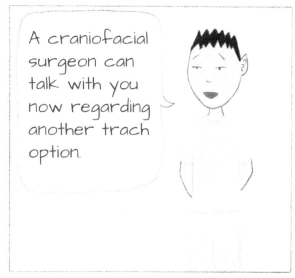

A craniofacial surgeon can talk with you now regarding another trach option.

95

Oh, Charlee. What do you want us to do?

98

CHAPTER 8
BARGAINING

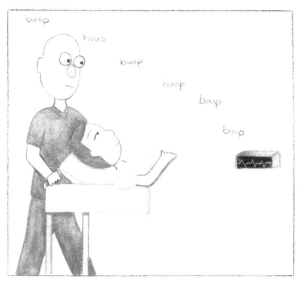

Hold the elevator!

So if a baby can go five days without an episode, the spell will break!

That means you could go home tomorrow!

Looks like we are going to the same place!

Have you given any thought to the trach?

We don't think it makes sense. Why would we put her through such a big surgery if the nasal trumpet does the same thing as the trach? Can't we just use the nasal trumpet if we need it?

You can't argue that the sleep study results are concerning. The attending and specialists all urge the trach.

If you will not consider our recommendations, I can connect you to the palliative care team.

FINE!

Is it okay to hold her?

She makes everything better. Do you want to hold Charlee?

No. I can't right now.

Come with me. I want to introduce you to someone.

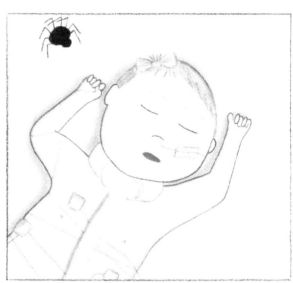

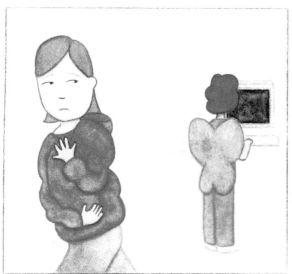

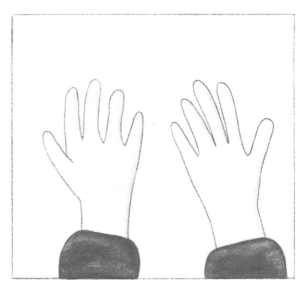

We have to get Charlee out of here.

I don't trust the care in this place anymore.

She would be better off at home with us.

We just have to be patient a little longer.

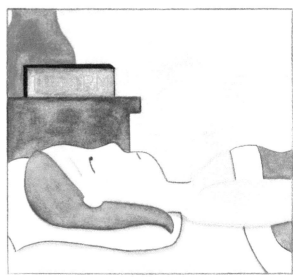
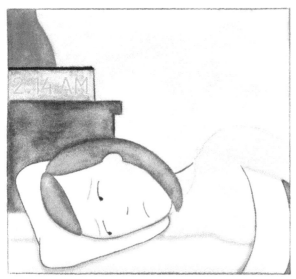

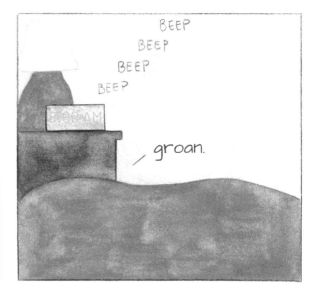

CHAPTER 9
UNDERSTANDING

Good morning!

What brings you to this meeting today?

Well...

We don't agree with the decisions made in the NICU.

I mean, we understand the concerns. it's just that the less invasive option works.

And furthermore, she had such a reaction after the first surgery.

We don't want to put her through that again.

Can I ask you...

What were your hopes and dreams for your daughter?

I had such fond memories of Girl Scouts as a kid.

When we found out we were having a girl, I was so excited because it meant that I could share that with her.

Is there anything we can do to help set up a good quality of life at home?

Can we have some support? Some nursing assistance?

Unfortunately, you don't qualify.

If you have a trach, you would.

It's okay. We'll do fine on our own.

Could we at least have a monitor?

I think we could arrange for that.

CHAPTER 10
DISCHARGE

Looks like day 48 is your day.

Time for us to get out of here.

Er... I mean, we are looking forward to being home for the holidays.

Do you have any questions?

Yes. Lots of questions. Do we get instructions for everything? Her feeding schedule? How to run her feeding pump? We are still getting a monitor, right? And a nasal trumpet to take home? The CPR protocol?

Yes. Yes. Someone wil help you out with all of that.

What's going on here?

She has to sit in her car seat for two hours without any problems to show it's safe to travel.

It's not going so well. She's thrown up and had a couple of desaturations.

I have a delivery for a feeding pump and a pulse oximeter.

That's us over here.

That car seat isn't going to work for her.

She's going to have to use this car bed.

Someone is waiting for you at the safety center to install it in your car.

Before the attending physician will sign off on your discharge, you need to do this last thing.

You need to show us you can insert this nasal trumpet in case of an emergency.

She's been throwing up a lot today. Maybe it's not a good idea to upset her.

Well, we can fix that. You need to slow down the feed rate on the pump over a longer period of time.

Go on. The sooner you get it in, the sooner you go home.

whimper

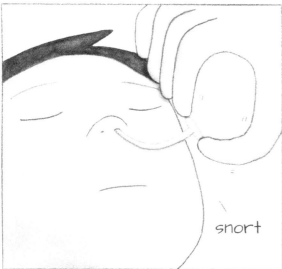

snort

wah!

What's going on?

I can't do it.

If the time comes, you will.

126

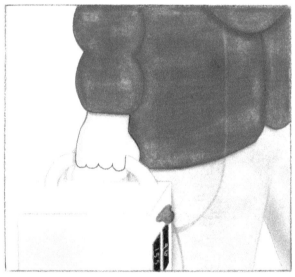

CHAPTER 11
RETURN

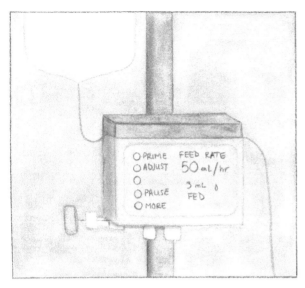

How many times did the alarm go off last night?

I stopped counting after the sixth time.

Get a nap today. I'll be back as soon as I finish the stuff at work that can't be put off.

I can't wait for the three of us to all be together.

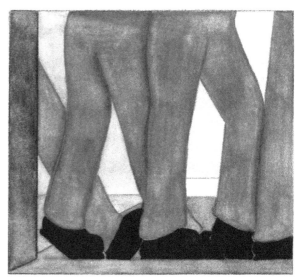

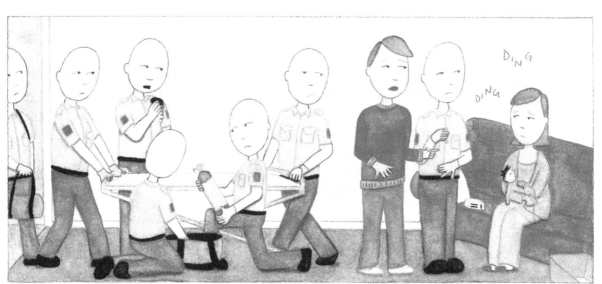

That's all? What did you do?

It's just oxygen. But we're all going to have to take a ride to the castle up on the hill.

Get your car so you have a way back. Meet us there.

Would...
Would this
have been
prevented if
she had a
trach?

No.
The airway
was open.

We are here.

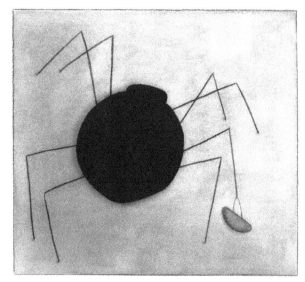

140

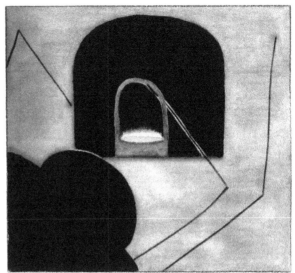
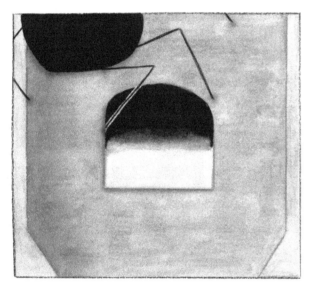
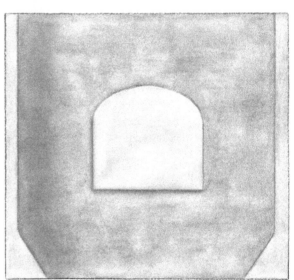

It wasn't it.

It couldn't help her.

It didn't break the spell.

Our love wasn't enough.

The spell won't break if you stay down here.

She may be back at the castle, but she needs you more than ever.

You know what's best for her.

You just have to trust yourself.

I would give anything to redo that one day she was home.

I would have spent every moment holding her tight.

choke

CHAPTER 12
ENDURE

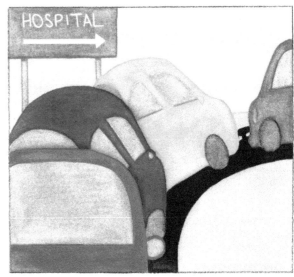

We're here to see Charlee.

She's not listed as inpatient here anymore.

There you are!

We'll come to wherever you need to be.

Welcome to the pediatric intensive care unit.

So nice to meet you! We've heard so much about you from the NICU team.

We are trying to understand the conditions and anomalies around what brought your daughter back here.

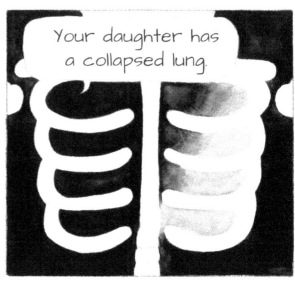

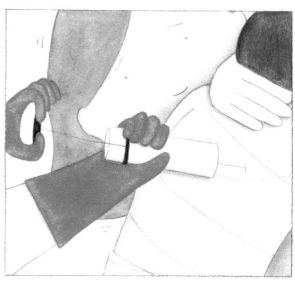

Hi there. I'm the pulmonologist that's been following your daughter's case since the NICU.

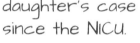

I reviewed her sleep study and, on paper, it showed she was obstructing.

But in person, I see it is not obstruction, but shallow breathing caused by the condition collapsing the lung.

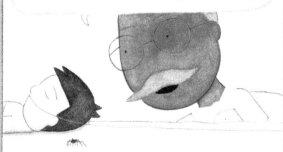

I am changing my previous recommendation for the tracheostomy. She does not need one.

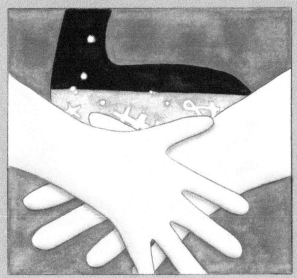

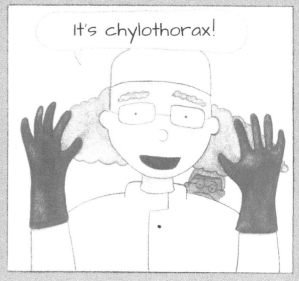

Hey.

Are you okay?

She doesn't need a trach.

What!?

It took every ounce of my being to stay composed.

What if we had gotten it and found out we didn't need it after all?

I would've lost it and you would be a single parent.

Isn't it great news that she doesn't need the trach?

We have some ideas to resolve the chylothorax.

The first option is surgery to give drainage in the lungs.

But she doesn't do well with the anesthesia.

The second option is to put her on a low fat, high calorie formula.

Giving her breast milk feels like the only thing I am doing for her at this point.

Please. It's so important for me to do this for her.

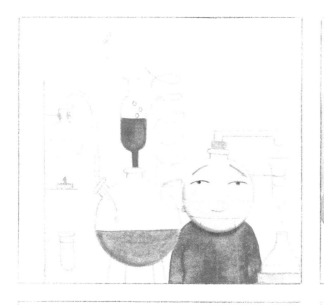

When milk sits in the refridgerator, it separates and rises to the top.

You are going to collect that milk under the fat.

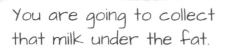

Good. Put the skimmed milk in a new container.

These will go back in the fridge for 24 hours. Then, skim these once more.

After that, you are going to add this formula to fortify it with calories.

Is it supposed to smell like this?

I know it's a lot of work, but she'll get good antibodies.

Are you going to enjoy some Thanksgiving dinner yourselves?

Oh, right. It's Thanksgiving.

You guys need to get some good nourishment yourselves.

You know, we do have two seats still open for us.

CHAPTER 13
A WAY OUT

You're both here! We're so glad you could make it.

We were just each saying what we are grateful for.

What are you grateful for?

I'm grateful that we are able to be here today.

I am grateful Charlee isn't having surgery today.

And she is alive today. We still have her with us.

I can't imagine everything you are going through.

I know next Thanksgiving will be different.

Aren't you enjoying yourself?

You seem distracted.

I can't seem to figure out how to break the spell.

It is not your spell to break. It's hers.

Your role is to make sure she knows she is loved.

Charlee, it's Mama and Daddy.

You should hold her. I think she would really like that.

I can't. I feel like I'm going to hurt her if I do.

Love is all we have right now.

And the only way we can get through this is together.

Okay. I can do that.

Alright, the OR is ready.

Wait a second! We are waiting on x-rays to confirm improvements in the lungs.

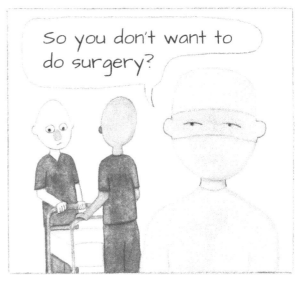

So you don't want to do surgery?

Not if we don't have to.

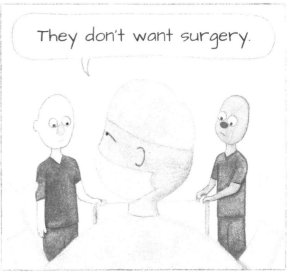

They don't want surgery.

You can see compared to the last x-ray there is improvement in the lungs.

Whew.

I'm really happy for you.

Just keep doing what you're doing and you'll be able to go home soon enough.

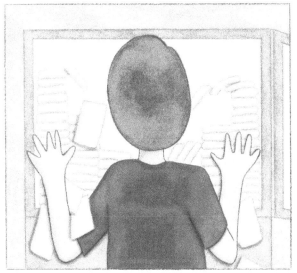

Don't you think there's enough milk in the freezer?

I was almost lost to a milk avalanche and never heard from again.

Now is the time to stock up before she comes home.

Besides, we'll have enough milk for coffee through the winter.

You're naked? That's how you could pull out your G-tube!

Hang on. Let's get some blankets and cover you up.

WARM BLANKETS

Are you mom of that adorable baby who's always alone?

That's me.

I've been telling my daughter, I feel so bad for that baby. No one around for her.

The pumping and the preparation keep me busy.

My daughter hasn't left her son's bedside since they got here six weeks ago.

You know, if you're so busy, I just might slip in to keep that baby of yours company.

You don't have to do that.

Her vitals look great.

Can parents stay overnight?

That bench over there is also a guest bed.

Okay. I will be staying here from now on.

That's a good idea. You can start learning her routine for when she goes home.

And if anything comes up, you want to get it with the suction.

Now we can get to the fun part of our bedtime routine.

Storytime!

So when Mama Grizzly and Baby Bear left the den...

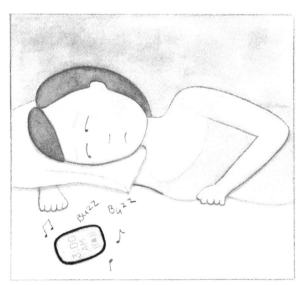

Here we have a two month female admitted fourteen days ago.

Chylothorax is improving with skimmed breast milk.

There is no longer concern for decline of the lung.

So we can start putting together a home care plan.

I need home oxygen ordered. And suction and a nebulizer.

Make sure they have enough feeding supplies for home use.

Get the dietician and respiratory therapist in here for instructions.

I want names and numbers for every specialty department.

And if Mom and Dad feel ready, they can take Charlee home today.

CHAPTER 14
RELEASE

This is the number to call when you need to order more feeding supplies.

Do these respiratory treatments three times a day.

The g-tube site looks good. Dress the area twice daily.

If saturation levels drop, try more oxygen. If levels don't increase, call 911.

Here is my contact info along with the numbers for all specialty departments.

Sign here if you understand how the suction machine works.

I'm just going to send you home with extra gauze.

These little syringes will come in handy for you.

And take a couple packs of diapers so you don't have to run out so soon.

I better get you a wagon.

The departing party favors are way better this time.

It's official. Here are your discharge papers.

You need to understand that her release is different from the others.

You will need to return to the castle from time to time.

And she is going to need to go home in the care of my guardian spider.

My spider will assist you as you continue her care.

It has been a pleasure caring for your daughter.

She really did choose us for a reason.

Look at how far we've come over these last two months.

I know we can do this together.

Together.

Acknowledgements

Thank you to Tisha West for your birth planning support. To Nurse Jenny and all of the other nurses who took good care of us. To Dr. Liu for your compassion towards our family in the PICU. Sarah Longfield Reppenhagen and all of the other friendly faces who made being in the hospital a little less cold. To my mom, Bonnie Smith, for staying with us while we hoped and cried and loved in the NICU. Kristin and Jason Tand for being there to pull us into the living world when we were drowning in the medical one. And to the friends and family who supported, loved and lifted us up bravely and endlessly. Sydney McIntosh, this story would have taken me at least 10 more years if it weren't for you. Ashlee Irwin for being an amazing case manager to Charlee. This book would not be finished and I would still be on hold getting nowhere in the medical system without you.

Thank you to Cassandra Grimes for being the catalyst for this project and for all of your family support. To Brenna Friesner for your introduction to watercolor pencils. To the artistically inclined folx at Collage PDX for your non-judgment and patience while helping me select supplies. To Aygul for encouraging me to deepen and grow my artistic style and for helping me see the vision. Jeanette Rawlins for helping me focus the story and find an ending. Emily Lewis and Mike Skrzynski for creating learning space to explore comic and illustration creation. To Ayn Frazee, Elizabeth Haigh and Sylvia Triplett for your fresh eyes. To the Independent Publishing Resources Center for providing a supportive community space. Amanda Blix for pointing me to Mutha Magazine. Jade Sanchez-Ventura at Mutha Magazine for bringing the short story of Release to public readers.

And thank you to Mark for your infinite love and support.

CPSIA information can be obtained
at www.ICGtesting.com
Printed in the USA
LVHW071737160122
708696LV00007B/172